This book belongs to:

oskar

I celebrated World Book Day 2020
with this gift from my local
bookseller and Scholastic
#shareAstory

CELEBRATE STORIES. LOVE READING.

This book has been specially created and published to celebrate **World Book Day**. World Book Day is a charity funded by publishers and booksellers in the UK and Ireland. Our mission is to offer every child and young person the opportunity to read and love books by giving you the chance to have a book of your own. To find out more, and for loads of fun activities and reading recommendations to help you to keep reading, visit **worldbookday.com**

World Book Day in the UK and Ireland is also made possible by generous sponsorship from National Book Tokens and support from authors and illustrators.

World Book Day works in partnership with a number of charities, who are all working to encourage a love of reading for pleasure.

The National Literacy Trust is an independent charity that encourages children and young people to enjoy reading. Just 10 minutes of reading every day can make a big difference to how well you do at school and to how successful you could be in life. **Literacytrust.org.uk**

The Reading Agency inspires people of all ages and backgrounds to read for pleasure and empowerment. They run the Summer Reading Challenge in partnership with libraries; they also support reading groups in schools and libraries all year round. Find out more and join your local library. **summerreadingchallenge.org.uk**

BookTrust is the UK's largest children's reading charity. Each year they reach **3.4 million** children across the UK with books, resources and support to help develop a love of reading. **booktrust.org.uk**

World Book Day also facilitates fundraising for:

Book Aid International, an international book donation and library development charity. Every year, they provide one million books to libraries and schools in communities where children would otherwise have little or no opportunity to read. **bookaid.org**

Read for Good, who motivate children in schools to read for fun through its sponsored read, which thousands of schools run on World Book Day and throughout the year. The money raised provides new books and resident storytellers in all the children's hospitals in the UK. **readforgood.org**

Tree-House Comix Proudly Presents

DOG MAN

WRITTEN AND ILLUSTRATED BY **DAV PiLKeY**

AS GEORGE BEARD AND HAROLD HUTCHINS

WITH COLOR BY JOSE GARIBALDI

AN IMPRINT OF

■SCHOLASTIC

Published in the UK by Scholastic Children's Books, 2020
Euston House, 24 Eversholt Street, London, NW1 1DB, UK
A division of Scholastic Limited.

London – New York – Toronto – Sydney – Auckland
Mexico City – New Delhi – Hong Kong

SCHOLASTIC and associated logos are trademarks and/or
registered trademarks of Scholastic Inc.

ISBN 978 1407 19987 0

A CIP catalogue record for this book is available from the British Library.

Printed by CPI Group (UK) Ltd, Croydon, CR0 4YY
Papers used by Scholastic Children's Books are made
from wood grown in sustainable forests.

1 3 5 7 9 10 8 6 4 2

www.scholastic.co.uk

DOG MAN

~~the~~ Behind the Scenes

One Time, George met Harold in kindergarten.

"nice to meet you."

"me too."

They became best friends and started making Comics.

Their very First Comic was a epic novella called:

The Adventures of DOG Man

FAKSHIN
LAFFS
TEARS
by George and Harold

Over the years, they made TONS of DOG Man Comic Books.

Then one day in 4th Grade, They got a new idea.

They started making a new comic.

Captain Underpants
By George and Harold

Soon, their lives got REALLY complicated!

There was Danger...

...HORROR...

ZAP!

..and ridiculously convoluted plot lines.

And just when it seemed like things couldn't get any worse...

Things got better.

Hey!

?

All the drama had come to a end.

But there were still lots of unanswered questions.

Where are our doubles?

Where's Tony, Orlando, and Dawn?

George and Harold searched their tree house for clues...	...but soon, they got distracted.
	Hey, Look! **aw, cool!**

It's a box full of ~~this~~ old Dog Man comics we made when we were kids.

Hey, I forgot all about these!!!

They read for hours

Ha Ha Ha Ha

I crack me up!

How about a Dog Man comic?

OK!

And together, the two friends wrote and drew and laughed all afternoon.

George tried to spell more better...

Dict-ion-ary

... Harold tried to draw more simpler...

... and thus, **DOG MAN** was reborn anewish!

class!

DOG MAN

Enjoy it!!!

DOG MAN
...our story thus far...

Hi, everybody! Welcome to our Second DOG Man novel!

This comic introduction will help ya get caught up on the epicness!

In a world where evil cats wreak Havoc on the innocent...

Haw Haw Haw!

...and Sinister villains Poison the Souls of the meek...

9

But then...

Haw Haw!

BOMB

a BOMB??? I'LL put my Best men on it!!!

chief

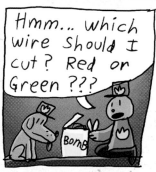

one Tragic BLunder Changed Their Lives Forever.

Hmm... which wire Should I cut? Red or Green ???

BOMB

Grrr!

OK! Green it is!!!

And So......

SNIP

Aw, man! I unwittingly created the Greatest cop of ever !!!!

And it was True. Dog man had the advantages of Both man ... and Dog...

...but There was a dark Side, too.

Dog Man had some very Bad habits.

He slobbered all over everybody...

aw, Gross!

chief

...he was obsessed with balls...

SQueak
SQueaK
SQueaK

13

...and for some weird reason, he liked to roll around in dead fish.

aw, man!

not again!

Dog Man, you are a awesome cop.

But you're a **BAD DOGGY!**

You better be a good boy...

...or you'll be in the **DOGHOUSE!**

Will our hero be able to overcome his canine nature and be a better man?

Or will his bad habits get the best of him?

Find out now!

If you like action...

...Suspense...

...Romance...

sniff

sniff

...and Laffs...

...Then DOG MAN is GO!

"DOG man is GO"? That don't make no sense!

But we **Like** it!

ENJOY !!!

16

Tree House Comix Inc. presents

DOG MAN
and The wrath of Petey

Action

Drama

Laffs

a epic novella by
George Beard and
Harold Hutchins

DOG man Was the Best cop of the world.

We Love you DOG man.

But He Had one weakness.

Trash

Hey, DOG man, Quit eating out of that Garbage can!

munch munch

and Quit rolling in that dead Fish!

and Quit sniffing that other DOG ~~DOG~~

19

21

Petey went on a crime spree

Haw Haw

He robbed Banks.

aw, man!

Jim's Bank

Jim

He stole Jewels

Gimme!

no fair

He even Hi-Jacked cars

STOP, thief!

Yee Haa

But No cops could ever catch him

Haw Haw

Gee, I sure wish DOG Man would come Back!

me Too.

22

meanwhile,
DOG man
was Hiding
in a alley

munch
munch

Trash
can

Then...

📰 NEWS ⭐

PETEY
RUns
amuck

BUT WHERE
is DOG man
huh?

Trash
can

DOG man Felt
ashamed.

He knew he
must Be Brave

So DOG man
Returned
BRavishLy
To save
the Day

DoG Man searched For Petey

Soon He Picked UP a Trail.

snif snif

IT Led Straight to Petey's Hideout.

snif snif snif

petey the world's most evilest cat

But it was a trap

guess what?

IT'S Bath Time

spray

Dog man got scared!

Come and Get it!

SOAP

He digged a hole to get away

Dog man Digged and digged

But Petey Followed Him down the Hole

Here I come

SOAP

DOG Man DUG aLL the way under the zoo.

nks | HIPPO | LiOn | eLephant

He came up in the skunk cage.

SSSS

SSSSS

27

PETEY RAN OUT OF THE HOLE

RIGHT INTO A COP'S NET

got-cha!

YOU'RE GOING TO JAIL, BUSTER!

rats!

FLIP-O-rama

Here's How 2 do it.

PUT YOUR Left Hand There on dofted Line

HOLD the other page With your thumb

Flip the Page Back and Forth

It makes it LOOK Like a moving cartoon

Left Hand Here

Bathtime
for
Dog man

RIGHT
THUMB
HERE

Bathtime
for
Dog man

Tree-House Comix Proudly Presents

DOG MAN

in

The TONGUE OF JUSTICE

ACTION

TRIPLE FLIP-O-RAMA

LAFFS

By George B. and Harold H.

DOG Man was the Greatest cop ever!!!

BUT he had some Bad Habits.

He Dranked out of the TOILeT.

He Licked himself in inapropreate plases.

and he threw up everywhere.

BLAP

34

SPLAP!

DOG MAN!!!

Later

Why You Gotta Bust my chops, huh?

You Better straighten up or else!!

Dog man promised to Be a better man...

...But could he be a better Dog?

35

36

Petey Sneaked to the police station...

COPS

and put a air Freshener in every cop car.

Haw Haw!!!

soon every cop will be my slave!!!

LATER

RING

HELLO?

theres a Bank robbery

where?

at the Bank!

Oh.

38

..Except one!

DOG MAN LiKed to drive with his head Out the window.

So he never Smelled the eviL air Freshener!

Dog man arrived at The Bank...

The BANK

... JUST as PeTeY was escaping.

UP the stairs they ran.

DOG MAN was getting super thirsty...

Then he saw it!!!

gLisTening... sparkLing... REFRESHing...

COOL as a mountain stream...

ThirsT QuencH- ing and DELICi- ous...

GLUG GLUG GLUG

Aaaaaaah!

Dog man ran up to the next floor.......

where a BIG surprise awaited for him.

HAW HAW HAW!!!

42

all cops are now my slaves!

Destroy Dog man! Yes, master Petey.

is this the end for Dog Man? of course it is!!!

Theres only one Antidote to my zombie Potion!

and I keep it safely hidden where nobody will ever find it...

...Downstairs in my shiny, white...

...Toilet Bowl!!!

DOG man had to act fast! So He thought Up a 3-Step plan.

FLIP-O-RAMA

Flip it---
Don't Rip it!!!

LEFT
Hand Here

Step 1

Retrieve the
Antidote

RIGHT
THUM
HERE

Step 1

Retrieve the Antidote

the anti-
dote was
on the
FLOOR...

BUT HOW COULD
He use it???

FLIP·O·RAMA

Left
Hand Here

Step 2

Collect the antidote

RIGHT
THUMB
HERE

step 2
Collect the
antidote

The antidote was on DOG MAN's tongue.

now came the ~~fun~~ FUN Part!!!

TRiPLE FLiP-O-RAMAS

animate the action cheesily. Heres How:

Hold Book open Like this...

FLip Page Back and Forth.

add your own sound Effects!

LEFt Hand Here

DOG Man Licked all cops faces.

and soon...

HEY!

chief

We ain't zom- Bies no more!!!

aw, man!

Aint you Glad you ain't no Zombie no more?

I sure amn't!

HOORAY FOR DOG Man!!!

chief

Rats!

ABOUT THE AUTHOR-ILLUSTRATOR

When Dav Pilkey was a kid, he was diagnosed with ADHD and dyslexia. Dav was so disruptive in class that his teachers made him sit out in the hall every day. Luckily, Dav loved to draw and make up stories. He spent his time in the hallway creating his own original comic books.

In the second grade, Dav Pilkey made a comic book about a superhero named Captain Underpants. Since then, he has been creating books that explore universally positive themes celebrating the triumph of the good-hearted.

ABOUT THE COLORIST

Jose Garibaldi grew up on the South Side of Chicago. As a kid, he was a daydreamer and a doodler, and now it's his full-time job to do both. Jose is a professional illustrator, painter, and cartoonist who has created work for many organizations, including Nickelodeon, MAD Magazine, Cartoon Network, Disney, and THE EPIC ADVENTURES OF CAPTAIN UNDERPANTS for DreamWorks Animation. He lives in Los Angeles, California, with his wonder dogs, Herman and Spanky.